Ayyám-i-Há in My Family

Written by Alhan Rahimi

Illustrations by Kseniia Pavska

Copyright © 2021 by Alhan Rahimi
(corrected version)
alhan@persianarabic.com

ISBN: 978-1-7770934-4-0 (paperback)
ISBN: 978-1-7770934-5-7 (hardcover)

Written by Alhan Rahimi.

Illustrations & cover by Kseniia Pavska

This book has been approved by the National Spiritual
Assembly of the Bahá'ís of Canada.

Ayyám-i-Há is approaching and I'm super excited!

I'm Maya and I will be celebrating Ayyám-i-Há next month. Everyone celebrates Ayyám-i-Há in a way that suits their family.

Our family starts by making a list of all the people we'll make gifts for, then making those gifts, and most importantly, wrapping them. I really enjoy wrapping the gifts and writing names on each one.

One year, we bought wooden frames and I colored them all.

What are some gifts that you can make?

Some families prefer to buy their gifts. That's okay too!

We also decorate our house with my paintings as well as some lights. Closer to the days of Ayyám-i-Há, we add balloons.

My friend Linda and her family like to make cards. My family sends our picture to family and friends as a card.

Last year, my mommy came to my school during Ayyám-i-Há and shared a story about it with my classmates. I gifted each of them a small gift.

My daddy told me that what's important about Ayyám-i-Há is to think of how we can serve those in our community who are in need. One way to help is to donate to the food bank. That's something we do every year.

Can you think of other ways to help those in need?

A few days before Ayyám-i-Há, I help my mommy bake some cookies and cupcakes. I love decorating them.

During Ayyám-i-Há, I get together with my friends and family when possible. First, we join the adults in saying prayers to thank our Creator for all that we have.

My friends and I usually do some coloring together and eat yummy food that our parents have made. We also exchange gifts.

I love dancing, so I ask my mommy to play some music, and we dance at home every morning of Ayyám-i-Há as well. I feel shy about dancing in front of my friends, but I might try this year.

It doesn't matter how you decide to celebrate Ayyám-i-Há. You can do one thing or many things. What matters is that you're happy during this time and that you think of how you can make others happy, too.

Happy Ayyám-i-Há !

Some facts about Ayyám-i-Há that is celebrated by Bahá'ís all over the world:

* Ayyám-i-Há is an Arabic phrase that means 'Days of Há' (Há is a letter in the Arabic alphabet that corresponds to H in English).
* Ayyám-i-Há spans four or five days of the year.
* These days are extra days to the Badí' calendar; therefore, they are intercalary days.
* They fall right before the month of fasting.
* They are a time of joy, celebration, and service, as we've seen in this story.

Other Books by the same author

Garden of Riḍván
The Story of the Festival of Riḍván
for Young Children

Written by
Alhan Rahimi

Mullá Ḥusayn
The Story of the Declaration of the Báb
for Young Children

Written by Alhan Rahimi

MY FIRST BAHÁ'Í ALBUM

Compiled by Alhan Rahimi

Roses Everywhere

Written by
Alhan Rahimi

Illustrations by
Alina Onipchenko

The Moon Was There
Glimpses from the Báb's Childhood
for Young Children

Written by Alhan Rahimi
Illustrations by Anahit Aleksanyan

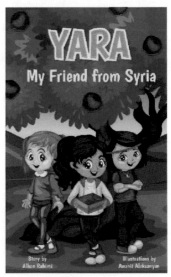

YARA
My Friend from Syria

Story by
Alhan Rahimi

Illustrations by
Anahit Aleksanyan